Contents

Foreword

Ensuring the health and safety of all employees is a critical responsibility. Learners on work placements, in particular, may be unaware of the hazards and risks that are present in all workplaces, and will require constant and consistent supervision and monitoring. This guide, the third in the ENTO 'Excellence' series, is designed to provide help and support for all those involved in assessing workplace health and safety, whether you are a health and safety assessor of employers and their workplaces, of learners on work placements or the designated 'competent person'.

ENTO is responsible for the national occupational standards for health and safety as well as for assessment and verification. We are acutely aware of the need for consistently high standards in risk assessment as much as in NVQ assessment, by both practitioners and their managers.

The ENTO national occupational standards are endorsed by the Health and Safety Executive and the professional body the Institute of Occupational Safety and Health (IOSH) and it is these national standards, designed for all employees as well as health and safety specialists, that underpin the guidance given here. This publication not only shows how the use of the national standards helps to determine competence and good practice, but also gives advice and information that is relevant to all workplaces, workers, supervisors, managers and employers.

Providing environments that are consistently healthy and safe, not only at work but also in social and personal settings, is an ambitious target. Achievement of this target will, however, greatly reduce the incidence of personal trauma and distress. It will also reduce costs to employers coming from lost production, adverse publicity, higher insurance premiums and possible litigation. It is intended that this publication will make a real contribution to meeting this target.

Tim O'Brien
Director, ENTO

Introduction

This guide is for everyone involved in assessing the health and safety of employers and their workplaces. It aims to help you judge whether a workplace meets health and safety requirements for learners (trainees, students, pupils and others) who are undertaking an element of work-based learning remote from their learning organisation or institution. If your job is to ensure that your learners are placed in safe, healthy and supportive working environments in which they can have a good-quality experience with the protection they need, this guide will help you get to grips with all aspects of the subject.

This section explains the benefits of good health and safety assessments, tells you when they are needed, and discusses the legal and funding requirements as well as the national standards. It also gives details of the five key principles that form the basis of good practice in making workplace health and safety assessments.

Who the guide is for

This guide is for you if you are:

- responsible for managing the health and safety of learners;
- managing work-based learning and work placements;
- the competent health and safety person;
- judging health and safety suitability at employer locations.

If you are new to health and safety assessment, this guide will help you understand your role and how it fits in with your own organisation's policies, the requirements of the Learning and Skills Council (LSC) and legal requirements. If you are an experienced health and safety assessor or manager, the guide will enable you to keep up to date with best practice resulting from recent changes to standards on learner health and safety. These include the LSC's introduction of health and safety procurement standards (HASPS) and their 2004 amendments to funding and contractual clauses.

The structure of the guide

This guide contains the following sections:

Introduction

This explains the key principles that underpin the guide and how to get the most out of it.

1 Managing assessment and assessors

This section looks at the management of health and safety assessments, including elements of:

- policy
- organising
- planning and implementing
- measuring performance
- review
- audit.

Such management principles should result in continuous improvement of assessment and assessors.

2 Planning for assessment

This explains what needs to be done before an assessment and includes a checklist for assessors to use.

3 Carrying out an assessment

This describes what a good assessment should cover, methods to use, observations to make and documents to check. It also gives some pointers to making a judgement and how to agree an action plan if a workplace fails its assessment.

4 Keeping records

This explains how and what to record during and at the end of an assessment.

5 Getting qualified

This tells you about the qualifications you can gain if you want to show your competence as an assessor. It gives information about training and support for assessors and organisations that employ assessors.

Further information

This section provides a glossary of terms used in this guide, and lists useful websites and publications.

Appendices

These contain a summary of the LSC's contractual clauses, the LSC's health and safety procurement standards, and an audit tool.

The benefits of effective health and safety assessment

The benefits of carrying out good-quality health and safety assessments are that you can.

- ensure that learners are in safe, healthy and supportive environments;
- satisfy legal obligations;
- satisfy the LSC requirements;
- ensure that arrangements made for learners provide for a good-quality learning experience and the transfer of essential health and safety knowledge (part of the LSC's safe learner concept);
- reduce potential losses and costs;
- provide confidence for the learner and support for the employer.

In order to achieve a good-quality and effective health and safety assessment it is essential to have a competent person carrying it out. The assessment should provide everyone involved with a level of comfort and confidence in the system, particularly the assessors themselves.

When is a health and safety assessment needed?

You will need to carry out a health and safety assessment whenever vocational learning has a work-based element remote from the learning organisation. This may include:

- apprenticeships;
- young apprenticeships;
- work experience and extended work experience;
- vocational learning support programmes;
- job trials.

An assessment must be undertaken before learning takes place or is funded. In some cases multi-sited organisations can use assessments to help them maintain consistent standards throughout their organisation.

You may also need to do an assessment when learners undertake developmental activities and trips. This guide does not deal with these, although they use some of the same principles.

Key principles

Five key principles form the basis of good practice
in health and safety assessment of workplaces.
They form the central themes of this guide.

1 Everyone responsible for health and safety assessments knows what is required and how to carry assessments out effectively.

This means:

- having a policy and procedures for assessment and communicating these to all staff;

- setting standards for assessment that satisfy legal and contractual or funding requirements and internal quality standards;

- ensuring that assessors are trained and competent to assess and have competent support.

2 Assessment focuses on the employer and location of the learning, while meeting the individual needs of the learner.

This means:

- talking to the employer about his/her health and safety arrangements;

- checking that risks have been assessed and control measures put in place and are working;

- briefing the employer on the learning and what it may mean for the employer and employees as well as what the learner is hoping to achieve;

- observing the working/learning environment and people working in and around the learner;

- agreeing and arranging health and safety controls for the individual learner, including those for effective supervision.

3 The result of assessment and agreements forms the basis for an action plan for improvement where necessary.

This means:

- identifying where standards have not been met or only partly met;

- making a decision on whether the employer/location should be:
  - recommended to be used for learning;
  - recommended but with an action plan;
  - not recommended.

- identifying with the employer any risks and control measures needed before a particular learner can start their placement.

4 The assessment process is an open and transparent one that, along with any action plan, is communicated to the employer.

5 The learner and the learner's supervisor are informed of the health and safety arrangements made.

This means:

- telling the employer or workplace in advance about the assessment process and what to expect;

- making clear the health and safety requirements in a written agreement;

- telling the employer the result of the assessment (the findings) whenever possible and appropriate;

- giving the employer a record (or summary) of the assessment and a written action plan;

- agreeing on the monitoring of the action plan and learner with the employer and/or supervisor.

This means:

- briefing the supervisor on the learning programme and what the learner is hoping to achieve;

- discussing and agreeing a health and safety learning plan;

- informing the supervisor whenever possible of any specific risks and control measures agreed with the employer;

- building a relationship with the learner's supervisor;

- giving the supervisor support and contact details in case of problems or concerns, or if the learner suffers a reportable incident.

Legal and funding requirements

When a learner is to be placed with an employer, your organisation has a legal duty for someone competent to assess the health and safety of the workplace to make sure it is suitable. This duty arises from:

- the Health and Safety at Work etc. Act 1974;

- requirements of the Management of Health and Safety at Work Regulations 1999 (as amended), including risk assessment;

- civil law, where the organisation placing a learner owes him or her a duty of care.

In addition to these legal requirements, the LSC contractually requires the organisations it funds to make an 'informed judgement about health and safety suitability' before it places or funds a learner (who may already be employed) in a location other than their own. Appendix 1 summarises the main LSC health and safety funding/contractual requirements.

The LSC also requires employers and environments to meet its health and safety procurement standard[1] for learner health and safety. The procurement standards are reproduced in appendix 2.

By following this guide to good practice and excellence in assessment, you should meet or even exceed all legal and contractual or funding requirements.

National standards

Two national standards apply to health and safety assessment:

1 the health and safety procurement standards (HASPS) set by the LSC as a minimum national benchmark for health and safety assessment applying to all those funded by the LSC;

2 the national standard for assessors as set out in ENTO-approved standards: Health and Safety for People at Work Unit D, 'Review health and safety procedures in workplaces'.

This guide will help you meet these national standards.

> The term 'assessment' is used throughout this guide, whereas the national standard of assessment uses the term 'review' and others previously have used the term 'vetting'.

---

[1] The procurement standard has been agreed in consultation with the HSE and DfES. Details are available on the LSC website and The Good Practice Toolkit for Learner Health and Safety website.

Flowchart for workplace assessment

This flowchart shows the seven stages you need to go through in order to make your assessment process an effective and efficient one. All the stages are discussed in detail in this guide.

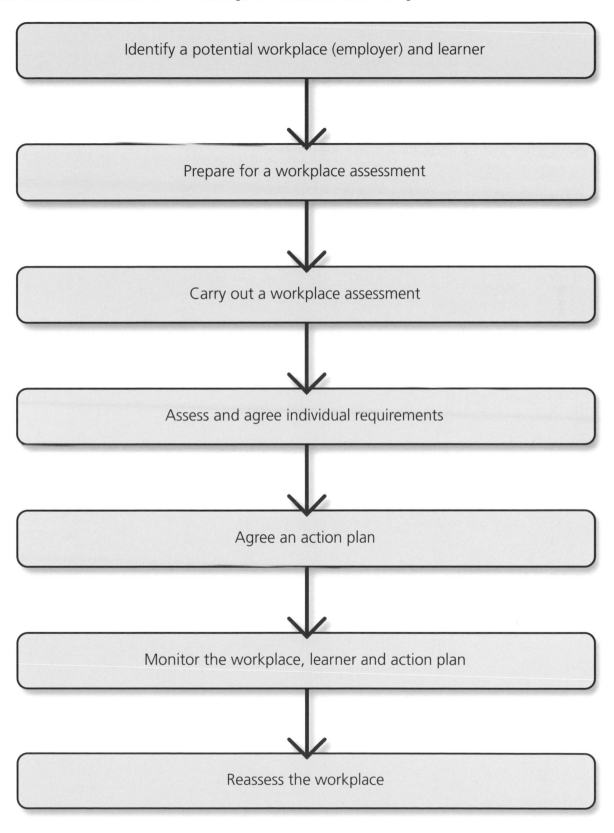

Identify a potential workplace (employer) and learner

Prepare for a workplace assessment

Carry out a workplace assessment

Assess and agree individual requirements

Agree an action plan

Monitor the workplace, learner and action plan

Reassess the workplace

1 Managing assessment and assessors

Health and safety assessment of workplaces should be part of your overall health and safety management system. It is a good idea to include learner health and safety in your general health and safety policy. Where learning is a major part of your business, learner health and safety needs to form a major part of your policy.

This section tells you how to put together a health and safety policy based on sound principles, and how to organise and manage the assessment process. It explains how to set targets that can be measured, checking them against the national standard, how to make agreements with sub-contractors, and how to monitor and review your procedures.

Policies for health and safety assessment

You will need to have a written policy that explains exactly what your procedures are for the assessment of workplaces, or cross-reference them to a quality manual. Your policy should reflect a commitment to learner health and safety and to ensuring a safe, healthy and supportive environment for learners. It should also:

- recognise the risk of placing your learners with others, particularly in work-based learning situations, and the need for good effective assessments;

- explain the organisation and responsibilities of people within your assessment process;

- outline your procedures for assessment, and give guidance on how to judge suitability of remote work-based learning environments.

Your policy will also need to include information on:

- the standard of assessment;

- the competence standard for assessors;

- what records to keep (and the issuing of certificates of assessment and/or certificates of achievement where appropriate);

- what action to take when standards are not met;

- your quality assurance arrangements for assessment;

- how and when your procedures will be renewed.

You should review your policy periodically and carry out audits to see whether the policy and procedures are working. As part of this approach it is important to consider setting some targets for assessment and the quality of assessments.

Health and safety management

Assessment affects all elements of any system. You can use the following flowchart as a framework for creating your own policy. This example is based on the flowchart in the Health and Safety Executive's (HSE's) publication *Successful* *Health and Safety Management* (HSG65). Other management systems you could use include ILO-OSH 2001 and OHSAS 18001 (BSI), *Specification for occupational health and safety management systems*.

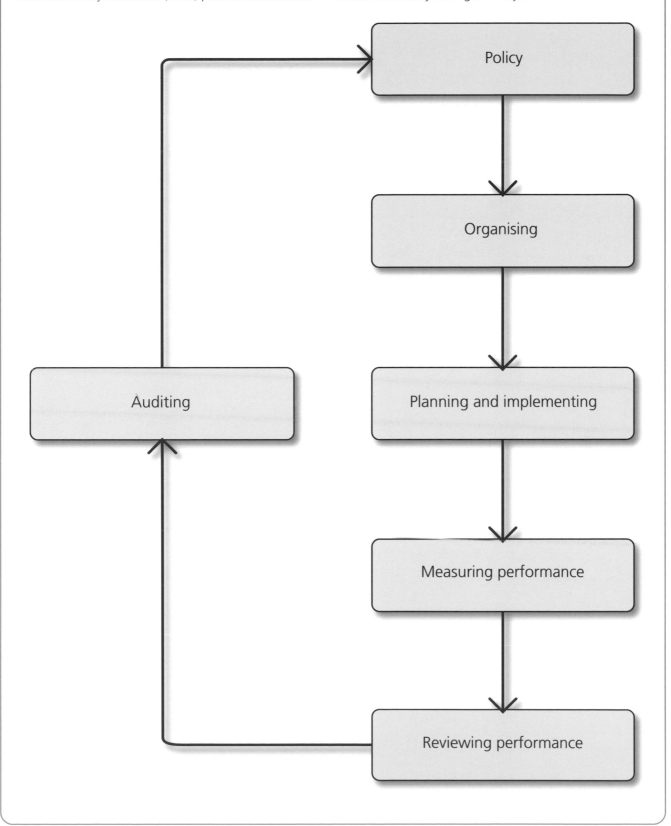

One organisation's safety policy for remote work-based learning

POLICY STATEMENT

Our general policy of ensuring a safe, healthy and supportive working and learning environment for learners extends to when learners are remote from ourselves, including when placed or learning with others. Our policy is to require the same high standards of others as of ourselves so far as is reasonably practicable.

ORGANISATION

To meet the above policy statement we will use competent persons to assess the health and safety suitability of all learning locations prior to any learning taking place. We will also make appropriate arrangements for the individual learner so as to meet their needs, including effective supervision. Remote learning will form part of our health and safety management system.

The Chief Executive has overall responsibility for learner health and safety. The Chief Executive will receive an annual report of learner health and safety performance that includes remote learning and the performance in assessing the suitability of employer locations.

The competent person (name) will review periodically the risks associated with external learning activities including work placements. The competent person is responsible for advising and drafting the procedures (control measures) to reduce the risks to learners so far as is reasonably practicable. The competent person will monitor and quality-assure the process of assessment.

Assessors of workplaces will be responsible for following the procedures and will be trained and authorised to assess to the standards described in the procedures.

The policy and procedures for assessment will be made known to all staff regardless of their role. This will be achieved through our initial induction process and line managers' health and safety briefings covering our policy and procedures.

RISK ASSESSMENT – PLACING LEARNERS WITH OTHERS

Incidents and accidents to learners over the years have identified the greatest risk to learners as being while they are under the control of others in a work-based learning situation. In work-based learning situations 10 reportable incidents have occurred, one of them a major classified accident, while only one reportable accident has occurred within our own premises.

The above statistics are consistent with national statistics produced by the LSC, showing that most accidents and incidents to learners occur in work-based learning situations.

In addition to the risk to learners there is a small risk to those who go out and assess the suitability of the workplace for learners. The normal risks of driving and working alone are dealt with elsewhere in this policy; however, some risk arises by being exposed to certain workplaces where health and safety may not be as well controlled as within our own premises.

PROCEDURES FOR ASSESSMENT (SUMMARY)

Procedures for assessment are set out in our quality manual and are summarised below:

- only persons trained and competent to ENTO Unit D will carry out assessments;

- the scope of assessment has been determined considering the risk involved and requirements to meet our duty of care and funding obligations;

- all assessments will be carried out prior to any learning being funded;

- all assessments will be recorded on our prescribed form;

- an action plan will be agreed and provided to the employer where standards have not been met or only partly met;

- a certificate of assessment or a copy of the assessment record will be issued to employers following assessment;

- for those meeting all the standards a certificate of achievement will be provided to the employer for the location;

- agreements will be made over the individual learner including the arrangements for competent supervision;

- the employer/workplace and learner will be monitored in line with our quality assurance procedures and based on risk and the needs of the learner;

- reassessment will take place every 1, 2 or 3 years depending on the risk of the workplace and learning activity.

MEASURING PERFORMANCE

Any incident with a work-based learner will be used to test how effective the assessment process has been. Any investigation into the incident will review the assessment and see what can be learnt. This forms part of our reactive monitoring procedures.

In addition to any reactive monitoring we will proactively monitor performance through the establishment of standards and targets for assessment. The procedures and detail are in our quality manual. The competent person as part of the above will review or quality assure 100% of all assessments and physically quality assure 5% of assessments by visiting the employer/location and the learner.

REVIEW AND AUDIT

To ensure that standards and targets are met and to ensure continuous improvement, we review and audit our performance and achievements formally on an annual basis. This is in addition to the ongoing monitoring.

An annual audit will be undertaken that will also bring together all information about the assessment process and measure the outcomes against our targets. This will include:

- survey with assessors;

- feedback from employers;

- feedback from learners;

- % achievement of various targets set;

- incidents/accidents and lessons learnt;

- other relevant information and matters.

A report will be produced with recommendations to improve performance as part of our policy of continuous improvement.

In your three-year development plan, where this is required by the LSC, it is good practice to include a summary of your health and safety strategy and policy. More guidance on three-year development plans is available from the LSC.

Assessing the risks of remote work-based learning

As with risk assessment generally, there are a number of ways to assess the risks associated with work-based learning when it is remote from your own organisation.

- **Examine your own statistics** of harm to learners. Did any occur to learners while they were with other employers? How does this compare with the number and rate of incidents when learners are with you?

- **Examine national statistics** of accidents and incidents to learners from the LSC. Most recent statistics show that most harm to learners (over 70%) occurs when they are in a work-based learning situation remote from their learning institution/organisation.

- **Carry out a theoretical risk assessment**, taking into account the following factors:
  - occupational area;
  - age and experience of the learner(s);
  - type of business (what they do);
  - size of business;
  - length of work-based learning element;
  - special needs of learner(s) including any medical health conditions;
  - the work and tasks to be undertaken by the learner;
  - any other risk factors.

The placing of learners with others will often pose significant risk, which needs to be recognised and recorded.

Although the health and safety risk of harm is a clear one, there are other risks, particularly if things go wrong, including:

- the risk of prosecution under the Health and Safety at Work etc. Act 1974;
- the risk of being sued by the injured party;
- the risk to reputation through adverse publicity;
- increases in insurance premiums;
- risk of LSC sanctions.

A good-quality assessment system will reduce all those risks as well as the risk of harm to learners. Putting in place effective control measures will not only protect you and the learner, but should also provide for a good-quality, safe and healthy learning experience.

Risks to assessors

While most of the assessment will relate to the learner, you must also assess risk to assessors at workplaces. Assessors will be able to exercise some control of the situation and be able to protect themselves through their own competence and understanding of risk and risk control in the workplaces they assess (one of the criteria of competence). Even so, you will need to ensure that assessors are protected by policies and procedures that cover, in addition to the general ones:

- providing personal protective equipment and clothing where needed;
- driving;
- remote/lone working.

Setting targets and measuring performance

Good-quality health and safety management requires the setting of targets that can be measured. You should be able continuously to improve standards as a result of actions taken.

You might want to set some or all of the following targets:

1   % of assessors competent against the national standard;

2   % of assessments carried out to our procedures and quality standards;

3   % of assessments quality assured by our competent person through discussion with the assessor;

4   % (e.g. 5%) sample quality checked;

5   % of employers/locations with an action plan;

6   % of the above followed up within timescales;

7   % receiving five days' notice of assessment, including a written briefing;

8   % of employers/locations provided with support;

9   number of requests for support from assessors;

10 % of positive feedback from surveys (both employers and learners).

You will need to set objectives and targets appropriate to your own circumstances and way of working. Everyone involved needs to understand the targets so that they can be measured. Normally, the competent person will continuously monitor achievement and use this information as part of any annual report and as part of self-assessment.

Procedures and standards

You will need to document your management system and procedures using a flowchart similar to that shown on page 13. Make sure that you explain procedures clearly so that everyone involved understands their role and what they need to do, particularly during the assessment process itself. The usual practice is to put the procedures in a quality manual or in the arrangements section of the safety policy (see above). This guide cannot write your procedures for you, but by working through it you should be able to put together effective procedures of your own.

To ensure good-quality consistent assessments, the standard and rigour of assessment are very important. To see whether you meet the national standard of assessment by the LSC, use the checklist on the following pages.

Self-check: general assessment standards

Use the following check questions (which relate to the national standards for general health and safety suitability) to pinpoint areas where you may need to improve your own assessment standards.

1 Do we check the safety policy?

Yes ☐   No ☐

if yes →

Does this cover:

- commitment? ☐
- responsibilities? ☐
- arrangements? ☐
- communication of policy? ☐

2 Do we check the risk assessment?

Yes ☐   No ☐

if yes →

Does this cover:

- significant risks identified? ☐
- recording of significant risks? ☐
- implementation of controls? ☐
- communication of risks and controls? ☐

3 Do we include accidents/ incidents and first aid?

Yes ☐   No ☐

if yes →

Does this cover:

- arrangements for first-aid materials? ☐
- arrangements for first-aid persons? ☐
- recording of accidents/incidents and first aid? ☐
- reporting of accidents and incidents? ☐
- communication of above arrangements? ☐

4 Do we check the effectiveness of supervision, information, instruction and training?

Yes ☐   No ☐

if yes →

Does it cover:

- provision of competent supervision? ☐
- health and safety induction? ☐
- ongoing information, instruction and training? ☐
- recording of information, instruction and training? ☐
- assessing and recording of the effectiveness of information, instruction and training? ☐

5 Do we check the provision and maintenance of equipment and machinery?

Yes ☐　　　　No ☐

if yes →

Does it cover:

- the standard of equipment provided? ☐
- the maintenance of equipment? ☐
- guarding and control measures? ☐
- electrical systems and equipment? ☐

6 Do we check the arrangements for personal protective equipment and clothing?

Yes ☐　　　　No ☐

if yes →

Does it cover:

- provision of ppe/c? ☐
- training in ppe/c use? ☐
- Enforcement of ppe/c use? ☐
- Maintenance and replacement of ppe/c? ☐

7 Do we check the arrangements for fire and other emergencies?

Yes ☐　　　　No ☐

if yes →

Do they cover:

- a means of raising the alarm? ☐
- fire fighting? ☐
- a means of escape and escape routes? ☐
- personnel for emergencies? ☐
- arrangements for tests and drills? ☐
- records/log of emergencies? ☐

8 Do we check the working/ learning environment?

Yes ☐　　　　No ☐

if yes →

Does this cover:

- the suitability of the premises? ☐
- the environment (temperature, lighting, space, etc.)? ☐
- welfare facilities? ☐

9 Do we check arrangements for managing health and safety?

Yes ☐　　　　No ☐

if yes →

Does this cover:

- consultation and communication with employees and their participation in it? ☐
- medical/health screening? ☐
- competent advice? ☐
- review of health and safety? ☐
- signs and notices? ☐
- notification to the enforcing authority? ☐
- insurance? ☐
- employees' capabilities? ☐
- working away/off site? ☐

Is anything missing from our general assessment standards check list?

What else do we cover that is not included in the general assessment standards self check list?

In addition to the general assessment, you will need an assessment and agreements for the individual learner. Again, you can compare your standards with those of the LSC in standard 10 of HASPS.

Self-check: learner assessment standards

Use the following check questions (which relate to the national standards for learner health and safety) to pinpoint areas where you may need to improve your own assessment standards for learners.

Do we ensure that:	Yes	No
1 the employer has assessed the risks to the learner/young persons?	☐	☐
2 the employer has put in place control measures as a result?	☐	☐
3 prohibitions and restrictions to the learner have been identified?	☐	☐
4 the learner is (or will be) competently supervised?	☐	☐
5 someone takes overall responsibility for the learner?	☐	☐
6 the provider provides induction and ongoing information, instruction and training that reflect the risk assessment?	☐	☐
7 the employer provides personal protective equipment and clothing where needed, and ensures its proper and effective use?	☐	☐

Is anything missing from our standards that is included above?

1

2

3

4

What in addition do we cover that is not included above?

1

2

3

4

To check the standards for assessors themselves, see section 5, 'Getting qualified' on page 57.

Agreements and contracts with subcontractors

It is good practice to have a written agreement or contract with an employer that makes clear that they are responsible for the health and safety of the learner. You should include the LSC contractual requirements in the agreement, which should at least cover the following:

- the requirement to:
  - report accidents and other incidents to both the enforcing authority and the funding organisation;
  - co-operate for reasons of learner health and safety including with the LSC if requested;
  - ensure that learners are always in safe, healthy and supportive environments, whether elsewhere, on site or when provision is contracted out;
- management of health and safety;
- promotion of the safe learner concept;[2]
- provision of information, instruction and training;
- assessment of health and safety understanding and its application, and recording the results of assessment;
- supervision;
- learner prohibitions and restrictions (where applicable);
- if a young person, the requirements in relation to child protection;
- compliance with all health and safety legal requirements and with regard to HSE-approved codes of practice and guidance.

Check your agreements with employers against the above points, and look at the agreement you have with the LSC. A sound agreement will protect you.

Quality assurance

An essential part of a good assessment system is quality assurance. Quality assurance of assessments will show whether the procedures are working, identify any problems and provide the assessors with support.

Quality assurance consists of two main elements:

- Someone other than the assessor needs to be responsible for checking the records of assessments. This is normally the assessor's manager or other competent person. A sample number (if not all) should be discussed with the assessor as soon as possible after the assessments themselves.

- In addition, a competent person will need to go and physically quality-assure a sample of assessments. This will entail visiting the employer and workplace and checking that the assessment was accurate and arrangements were as they should have been. This is best done as part of a monitoring visit to save time and avoid appearing too bureaucratic to the employer.

Another method of quality assurance is to swap assessors when reassessing, so that a different person assesses the employer or location each time.

---

[2] The LSC's safe learner concept is about the learners developing a practical understanding of health and safety through competent supervision, in a safe, healthy and supportive environment (see www.safelearner.info).

In addition to quality assurance procedures, it is a good idea to ask for feedback from the employer or person who helped you with your assessment. You should also ask your learners for feedback about the effects on them of the assessment process.

Using questionnaires

A follow-up letter to any assessment could usefully include a questionnaire or survey about the process. Your questions should reflect your own procedures and standards for assessment, but might include the following:

		Yes	No
1	Was the assessment pre-arranged?	☐	☐
2	Was a date and time agreed and did the assessor present him/herself at that date and time?	☐	☐
3	Was it made clear why the assessment was being undertaken and what the assessment would entail?	☐	☐
4	Did you receive a pre-assessment letter (or email)?	☐	☐

5 How did you rate the pre-assessment arrangements?

very good ☐   good ☐   satisfactory ☐   poor ☐   very poor ☐

6	Was the assessor presentation professional and appropriate?	☐	☐
7	Was the assessor helpful?	☐	☐
8	Did the assessor give you any support materials (where applicable) such as HSE leaflets?	☐	☐
9	At the end of the assessment did the assessor provide feedback on the assessment?	☐	☐
10	Did you agree an action plan?	☐	☐

11 How long did the assessment take?

12 Overall, how would you rate the assessment?

very good ☐   good ☐   satisfactory ☐   poor ☐   very poor ☐

Use these questions as a starting point to formulate your own quality assurance survey.

2 Planning for assessment

A good-quality assessment needs good-quality planning and preparation. Assessors need to plan not only for their own organisation's purposes but also for the benefit of the employer and location being assessed. You may need to explain to the employer why a health and safety assessment is required and how they might plan for your visit. Employers who understand what you have to do will normally prepare, and this will make your assessment quicker and more effective.

This section tells you what you need to know when planning your visit, and what you can do in advance to make the visit itself more successful.

Initial preparations

There are many things to think about and remember when you are planning for assessment. You need to know why you are carrying out the assessment, how long you expect it to take, and whether it is specific to one learner or more general. If it is specific, you will need to make sure you know everything relevant about the particular learner.

Self-check

To make sure that you have prepared and planned everything, use the following checklist.

Question	Yes	No
■ Am I competent to assess?	☐	☐
■ Do I understand our policy and procedures?	☐	☐
■ Do I know who to go to for support, help and advice?	☐	☐
■ Do I know where I am assessing, the name and address of the employer and the person(s) I am seeing?	☐	☐
■ Am I authorised to carry out the assessment?	☐	☐
■ Do I know the type of business it is (main activities)?	☐	☐
■ Do I know the size of the business (how many employees and how many at the place I am assessing)?	☐	☐
■ Has the employer/location been assessed before? (if yes, by whom and what was the result)?)	☐	☐
■ Do I know how to get there (safely)?	☐	☐
■ Do I know who the learners are (their age, experience, medical conditions, special needs etc.)?	☐	☐
■ Do I know what learning the learner is to undertake?	☐	☐
■ Have I checked HSE's database on notices and prosecutions in respect to the employer/location?	☐	☐
■ Have I checked with any other database about the employer and health and safety?	☐	☐
■ Have I properly briefed the employer?	☐	☐
■ Have I sent a letter or email confirming the date and time of the visit (where appropriate)?	☐	☐
■ Have I provided other relevant information to the employer?	☐	☐
■ Have I got the necessary documentation ready for the assessment?	☐	☐
■ Have I got the documents to record the assessment and action plan?	☐	☐
■ Have I got certificates of assessment and achievement (where applicable)?	☐	☐
■ Do I know who I need to see to discuss/agree health and safety matters?	☐	☐
■ Does anyone else need to be informed of my assessment?	☐	☐
■ Have I got support materials for the employer?	☐	☐
■ Do I know the normal significant risks and control measures for the type of employer/workplace to be assessed?	☐	☐
■ Am I dressed appropriately to give a professional image including having any necessary personal protective equipment and clothing?	☐	☐
■ Is there anything else I need in order to prepare for assessments?	☐	☐

Arranging the visit

You'll need to arrange the visit in advance with the workplace employer, and explain exactly what it will entail. Once you have made arrangements it is advisable to put them in writing, and send your letter or email in good time to the relevant person at the workplace (see the example on the following page). You can include any enclosures or attachments that will make clearer what is required.

In preparing for assessment, take into account your own health and safety needs. Ask the employer if you need to bring personal protective equipment or clothing and whether you need to be aware of anything else (such as vicious guard dogs).

Remember...

Although many employers will try to put you off at certain times of the year when they are very busy, this is probably a good time to arrange an assessment. You will learn more at busy times than during a quiet period. It is important to get a true reflection of how things are.

The pre-assessment letter or email

Here is an example of a letter or email to send to the employer before you do an assessment.

Dear (insert name)

Thank you for agreeing to see me on (date, time) at (location).

We wish to ensure the best-quality learning (or training) for (name of person/potential learner) and I would like to discuss a number of matters with you including the health and safety arrangements in your company and for (name).

Our own quality-assurance procedures require us to assure ourselves of the following matters where applicable:

- safety policy;
- risk assessments;
- arrangements for first aid and accidents;
- training, information, instruction and supervision;
- equipment and machinery;
- personal protective equipment and clothing;
- fire and emergency arrangements;
- the learner's workplace/environment;
- insurance and competent advice.

I have included our record of assessment so you can see what is required. I also enclose the leaflet from the Learning and Skills Council (who fund the learning) on their health and safety standards. Our assessment is not an inspection but a process to determine that the learner will be in a safe, healthy and supportive environment. It is also intended to be useful and beneficial to you, and I hope we can help you where we can.

I have also included our (detail your particular information/guidance about yourself and your organisation).

If you are uncertain of anything I will be pleased to assist you and you can contact me if you wish before my visit (state details).

Yours sincerely,

Jim Smith
Assessor

Advance agreements

To make your visit more efficient and prevent a possible wasted visit, you can raise a number of matters in advance. Some of these are to do with health and safety standards or requirements that, if not met, would prevent learning taking place. They include insurance, risk assessment and supervision.

Insurance

If the employer has no employer's liability insurance (ELI) or other necessary insurance, the learning will not be able to go ahead. It is therefore very useful to check initially and if possible get a faxed copy of the ELI insurance certificate. If you turn up on the day, carry out the assessment and then find out that no current ELI is in place, you will have wasted a lot of time and effort.

Risk assessment

If the employer says he hasn't carried out any risk assessments or is unwilling to carry any out, you will be able to avoid a wasted visit and assessment.

Supervision

As this is vitally important, try to find out in advance whether the employer is willing and/or has someone competent to supervise. If the employer is reluctant to provide effective supervision (or any at all), this suggests that it is not going to be a suitable, safe, healthy and supportive environment.

Many other matters may come up in conversation, for example asking who the competent person is, as this is often the best person for you to see.

Remember…

Without a competent person to supervise – one of the main standards – a workplace is unlikely to be suitable for learning.

You should ask whether the employer/location has other learners, or has been recently assessed by anyone else. If you can find out by whom, check with that organisation whether there were any problems and what the result of the assessment was (they may have left a certificate or record of assessment or achievement).

3 Carrying out assessment

You need to be satisfied that the workplace you are assessing is a safe, healthy and supportive one and that the arrangements for the learner will be at least satisfactory, or better if possible. As such there are a number of things to do, see and check. What is important is how this is done, and good communication skills are vital here.

This section describes what a good assessment should cover, the methods to use, observations to make and documents to check. It gives advice on how to make a judgement about whether the workplace is suitable, and on how to put in place an action plan if the location fails to meet some of the requirements.

Your approach

Assessing the health and safety suitability of a workplace and employer is less about inspection and checking documentation and more about your approach. It is vitally important to engage with the employer, using good communication and interpersonal skills. When assessing a small-sized employer, you will need to pay particular attention to the needs of that employer and the business, which may not have the sophisticated systems of a larger organisation.

If you are kept waiting in reception, take the opportunity to visit the toilet and see what the welfare facilities are like. This will tell you a lot about health and safety standards. Clean and tidy toilets show that the organisation takes pride in keeping the place in good order. This pride is likely to spill over into health and safety.

One of the things you need to be able to do is to sell the benefits of health and safety to the employer if they are in any doubt. You need to believe in the benefits yourself, and there is plenty of help on HSE's website as well as in this guide and elsewhere. You might remember the saying from the Easyjet founder, 'If you think health and safety is expensive, try an accident', but there are many reasons for promoting health and safety other than financial ones.

The following table shows the dos and don'ts of communication to bear in mind when you carry out an assessment.

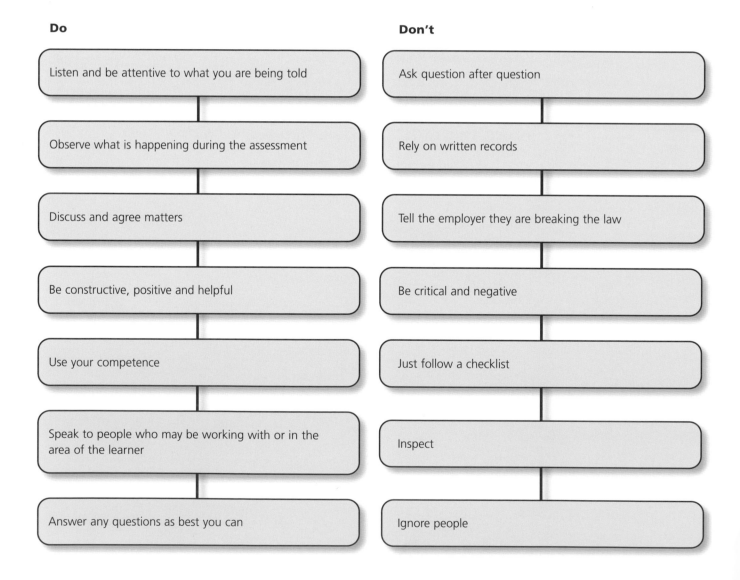

Do	Don't
Listen and be attentive to what you are being told	Ask question after question
Observe what is happening during the assessment	Rely on written records
Discuss and agree matters	Tell the employer they are breaking the law
Be constructive, positive and helpful	Be critical and negative
Use your competence	Just follow a checklist
Speak to people who may be working with or in the area of the learner	Inspect
Answer any questions as best you can	Ignore people

Methods and techniques

The first thing *not* to do is to go and sit in an office and go through a number of questions on a checklist. Engage the employer by discussing the business and what goes on, and asking to be shown around the workplace. Take an interest in the employer and what the business is about. Since you will gain a lot of useful information from this it is a valuable use of time, not a waste of it.

Although you may have a checklist or *aide-mémoire*, you should not be driven by it but by your own competence and skills to make a judgement on suitability. This is not always easy. For example, if everything appears to be in place but the attitude of the manager or supervisor gives rise to concern, this may be enough for you not to recommend the workplace. The difficulty is telling the employer!

If you are waiting in reception and the insurance certificate is displayed, take a note of the details – it will save you having to ask later to see it. You might also observe certain signs and notices in the reception area, or even when you parked, that will give you an early indication of suitability. If you are given a visitor's badge that includes health and safety rules such as what to do in the event of a fire, this is also a good indicator.

What to see/observations

When you are shown around the workplace there are certain things to notice that will show whether the workplace is a well-managed, safe and healthy environment. Observations should include:

- **Fire and emergency arrangements**
  - Are fire doors marked and clear?
  - Are fire signs and notices displayed?
  - Are fire routes free from obstruction?   could you and others get out safely?
  - Can you see fire-fighting equipment placed around the premises?

- **Floors and stairs**
  - Are they sound, level and free from obstruction?
  - Are treads sound?
  - Are there any tripping or slipping hazards?

- **Welfare facilities**
  - Are they present?
  - Are they clean and tidy?

- **The state of the premises**
  - Are fixtures and fittings in a good state of repair?
  - Is the workplace clean and tidy?
  - Is the lighting and general atmosphere good?

- **Safety signs and notices**
  - For example, is there a health and safety law poster: 'What you should know'?

- **Equipment and clothing**
  - Are employees wearing any necessary personal protective equipment and clothing?

- **The state of machinery and equipment**
  - Electrical equipment (any damage and disrepair?)
  - How people are moving around the workplace and interacting with one another.

Make your own list of the things to look out for in the type of environment that you will be inspecting. To be able to do this you need to know the main risks and the main control measures for the type of workplace and/or industry you are assessing. For example, on a building site you will need to observe that ladders are at the correct angle and secured properly.

If you are an inexperienced or less skilled assessor, your checklist or *aide-mémoire* will help you remember. If you cannot see things that you feel should be in place, ASK. However, it is not your job to check the dates on all fire extinguishers or that the first-aid kit has all the safety pins needed. Keep to your job of assessment.

The extent of any assessment will depend on the circumstances of the work placement. You'll need to use both common sense and your competence to decide what you need to see. For example, in a local authority civic centre, if the learner is in the Housing Department on the third floor, concentrate your assessment here. In contrast, you will need to extend an assessment beyond an office if, for example, a learner undertaking administrative duties in the offices of a warehouse needs to walk through the warehouse to collect documents from the goods in/out area. As such the greatest risks he or she may be exposed to will not be in the office but in the warehouse, and the safe management of fork-lift truck use will be relevant.

Remember...

Your record of an assessment and any certificate of assessment provided needs to reflect the areas assessed and observed.

Documents to check

Certain documents will give you additional confidence that health and safety is well managed, with significant risks identified and control measures in place.

Remember...

Good documentation does not in itself make an employer or location suitable. You'll need to make sure that any policy is understood and put into practice in the workplace.

Risk assessments must produce good and effective control measures that are effectively implemented. Your observations should help to confirm that this is happening, and discussions with others will certainly give a better indication of suitability.

Organisations with less than five employees are not required to have a written safety policy or to record significant findings from risk assessments. However, you still need to be satisfied that they are committed to health and safety, that they have assessed risks and put controls in place. Without written documents you need to satisfy yourself of those things through your discussions and observations.

It is best to view any documents as and when they arise in the visit around the workplace, and again at the end of the assessment.

Who to see

Before you can plan what you are going to ask, you need to know who you will be seeing. During an assessment you will normally speak to the following people:

- the manager or owner of the business;
- the competent person;
- the learner's intended supervisor;
- the person who will have overall responsibility for the learner and their learning (if not also one of the above);
- others doing a similar job or in the area where the learner will be;
- the learner (depending on the circumstances).

Remember...

Before making any visit, make sure that there is someone appropriate who is available to see you.

What to ask about the workplace

It is important to listen carefully to the feedback from the people you speak to, so that you can tailor your questions to that person, to ensure that they understand you clearly. Your standards and checklist will help you here, but you cannot pre-prepare everything. As you carry out assessments, observe and receive feedback, you may have additional questions – this is all about being competent.

You should ask both open and closed questions. Don't ask leading questions such as 'You have done risk assessments, haven't you?' You are unlikely to get a negative response.

Where you ask questions is also very important. Certain environments may be unsuitable because of noise, and if someone is working you do not want to distract them if they need to concentrate – they may have an accident if you do!

Some of the things you may ask will be with the aim of satisfying yourself that people:

- take health and safety seriously;
- understand and adhere to safety policies and procedures ;
- understand the risks and control measures that they need to;
- are consulted and involved in health and safety matters;
- know what they are doing and how to do it safely;
- know who to report health and safety problems to;
- know who the competent person is and any safety representative;
- have the correct equipment and get training and instruction in its use;
- know what they can and can't do, and have up-to-date information.

What to ask about the learner

In some cases the learner will be already employed at the workplace being assessed. In this case, it is appropriate to find out about the learner, including his or her:

- age;
- experience;
- medical conditions;
- special needs;
- programme/initiative;
- learning objectives;
- risk relevant to the learner and the learner's environment;
- induction, supervision, prohibitions, personal protective equipment and clothing, hours and breaks, risk and risk control.

If a learner is being placed, you should if possible know the learner or about the learner so that you can assess whether the workplace is suitable for that particular learner as well as its general suitability. In the case of work experience and some other programmes, the school or college will need to liaise closely with the assessment organisation and the employer. At the end of any assessment you need to be confident that the employer will be able to manage health and safety for your particular learner.

General arrangements

You will need to discuss a number of topics with the workplace employer. These include:

- the general learning and specific health and safety learning the learner has or will receive (agree a health and safety learning or training plan);
- any areas the learner is not allowed to go into or activities he or she will not be allowed to do (prohibitions and restrictions);
- the supervision arrangements for the learner (see below);
- what personal protective equipment and clothing the learner will need and how its use will be enforced;
- the information, instruction and training the learner will get, including the induction (where applicable);
- any additional controls that apply to the learner as a result of any health or medical condition or other special needs the learner may have (the school or college may need to advise).

You will need to agree on the arrangements for all these aspects of the learner's placement.

Remember...

Discussions and agreements need to focus on the young person's risk assessment and control measures. In some cases employer workplaces may be generally suitable for learners but not suitable for a particular learner with special needs.

Supervision arrangements

One of the most important aspects of assessment is to make sure that you can agree on an effective, competent supervisor for the learner. A number of LSC documents will help you understand better the role of the supervisor. In addition ENTO is developing a national standard for the competence of those who supervise the health and safety of learners.

In agreeing and making arrangements for supervision, it is a good idea to discuss the supervision requirements for each individual, bearing in mind the learner's:

- age;
- experience;
- special needs;
- medical or health conditions.

The supervisor needs to be aware of the learner's job description, prohibitions and restrictions and the risk assessment. It is also important that the supervisor or supervisors have the time and skills to do the job of supervising. It is not just about keeping the learner safe from harm, but also about giving essential health and safety information to the learner and checking that the learner understands and puts it into practice.

Remember...

Even a skilled tradesperson with over 20 years' experience may not necessarily be a good supervisor.

When you are making your decision, discuss with the employer some of the following:

1 Does the intended supervisor have the time to supervise the learner properly? (this can be particularly important if the person is on output bonuses and the learner may slow him or her up);

2 Does the supervisor want to supervise and look after the learner?

3 Does the supervisor know enough about health and safety?

4 Does the supervisor understand how people learn and the different types and preferred types of learning?

5 Does the supervisor understand young people?

6 Does the supervisor have the communication and interpersonal skills?

7 Are there any child protection issues if this applies?

8 Who will substitute for the supervisor if ill, on holiday or absent for any other reason?

The supervisor has a number of roles, and it is worth while discussing these with the employer and/or potential supervisors.

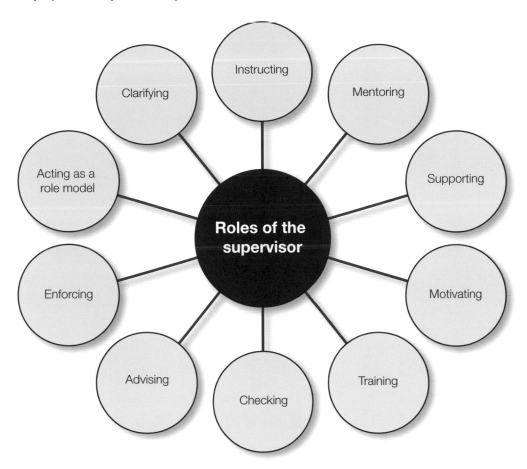

LSC's pocket guide to supervision provides more detail. It is good practice not only to provide the guide but go through some of the other guides to supervision.

Deciding on suitability

Deciding whether a location is suitable for your learner in terms of health and safety is not one to be taken lightly. At the end of an assessment (and sometimes afterwards) you will need to rely on your competence as to why a decision was made one way or another.

When you make your decision, you normally have three options:

1   recommending approval of the workplace/employer as it meets all the health and safety requirements/standards;

2   recommending approval of the workplace/employer as most of the health and safety standards have been met or at least partly met, and there are no immediate significant risks to the learner;

3   not recommending approval of the workplace/employer as some of the standards have not been met, and/or there is a risk or risks to the learner that are not sufficiently well controlled.

Unsuitable locations

Some standards and requirements are so important they would individually prevent learning being recommended. This is the case when:

- there is no insurance in place;
- risk assessments have not been carried out or significant risks have not been identified (when they should have been);
- there is no competent advice or access to competent advice;
- there is no commitment to health and safety;
- control measures have not been implemented and as a result significant risks are not properly controlled;
- effective supervision cannot be agreed and/or put in place;
- equipment or machinery (or anything else) is identified as dangerous;
- there are inadequate procedures for fire/emergencies;
- the employer does not ensure that health and safety rules (such as the use of personal protective equipment and clothing) are followed;
- the employer and/or key employees display a poor attitude towards health and safety, the learning or the learner.

You may also find that you cannot recommend the location if a number of smaller requirements and standards have not been met, or only partially met. When you feed back your findings and your recommendation at the end of the assessment, you need to be open and honest with the employer or their representative.

Remember...

It is good practice to leave a copy of the assessment record and ask the employer to sign and date it as a true record. The employer cannot then suggest later that things were otherwise than in the record.

Action plans following assessment

Most employers and workplaces are not perfect, and will fail to meet some of the requirements or standards. In such cases you will need to agree an action or development plan with the employer. Your competence as an assessor includes being able to put forward reasonable and sensible suggestions.

While it is important to be helpful, it is not your job to give 'competent person' advice or specific advice on what to do. The action or development plan must belong to the employer. Even so, if the employer does not have a pro-forma action or development plan of their own, it's a good idea to provide one. The plan should have all or some of the following headings:

1 Issue identified	3 Measurable outcome	5 Who is responsible for the action	7 Monitoring of the action
2 Action needed	4 How the action will be achieved	6 Date of completion	8 Cost and resources

The action or development plan needs to be agreed and put into writing, either at the time of the assessment or later. Section 4, Keeping records, gives an example of an action plan with some of the above headings.

Monitoring

Although assessment does not include monitoring, to be competent as an assessor you need to understand what monitoring is and when to use it. You will have to decide what monitoring will be required when you develop a post-review follow-up.

Monitoring involves both the workplace/employer – and particularly any action plan – and the learner. It is vital that someone within a reasonable length of time checks to see that the learner has settled in and that all the arrangements are working as discussed and agreed.

4 Keeping records

It is important to keep a record of every assessment you carry out, and to give a copy to the employer or workplace where the learner is going to be. Keeping records ensures that the assessment process is transparent – everyone can see the reasons for the assessment decision – and can be tracked.

You will need to develop your own record forms, which you can also use as a reminder of what to cover when you carry out an assessment. This section tells you what to record during and after an assessment, and gives examples of types of form to use, both for your own records and for the employer.

Types of record form

You will need to write your own record forms, which can double as prompts for assessors. Examples of how your records might look are shown on the following pages. Use them as a basis for developing your own. These particular examples are:

1 **General health and safety assessment** This is a record of the general assessment of suitability for the workplace, based on the LSC's HASPS (standards 1–9);

2 **Health and safety action plan** This is for use after the assessment has identified a need for action;

3 **Assessing health and safety for the learner** This is a record of the assessment in relation to the learner, based on the HASPS standard 10. It has its own action plan.

Remember...

It is important not to use a form as a checklist, as it is easy to fall into the trap of being driven by the form alone, and the perception that it all needs filling in with all positive responses.

Form 1: General health and safety assessment

Employer details

Employer's name:

Number of employees:

Nature of business:

Workplace address:

Main contact
(name & tel. no.):

Health and
safety contact:

Learner(s):

Supervisor(s):

Type of work carried out at workplace location:

Enforcement action (prosecutions, notices):

Health and safety committee/safety representation:

General health and safety assessment (continued)

Health and safety standards

1	Health and safety policy	Yes	No	Evidence/comments
A	Is there a clear commitment to health, safety and welfare (written policy statement when five or more employees)?	☐	☐	
B	Are the responsibilities for health and safety clearly stated (recorded when five or more employees)?	☐	☐	
C	Are arrangements for health and safety clearly stated, including the control measures identified from risk assessment (recorded when five or more employees)?	☐	☐	
D	How are the commitment, responsibilities and arrangements for health and safety (in 1A–C above) communicated to employees?	☐	☐	

Assessment of Standard 1: Met ☐ Part met ☐ Not met ☐

2	Risk assessment and control	Yes	No	Evidence/comments
A	Have risk assessments been carried out and significant risks identified?	☐	☐	
B	Have the significant findings and details of any groups identified as being especially at risk been recorded (mandatory where five or more employees)?	☐	☐	
C	Have control measures been identified and put in place as a result of the risk assessments?	☐	☐	
D	How are the risks and control measures explained to employees and others?	☐	☐	

Assessment of Standard 2: Met ☐ Part met ☐ Not met ☐

General health and safety assessment (continued)

3	Accident, incidents and first aid	Yes	No	Evidence/comments
A	Have adequate arrangements for first-aid materials been made?	☐	☐	
B	Have adequate arrangements for first-aid persons been made?	☐	☐	
C	Are accidents and first-aid treatment rendered recorded?	☐	☐	
D	Are or will all legally reportable accidents, incidents and ill health be reported to the enforcing authority and investigated?	☐	☐	
E	How are the arrangements for accidents, incidents, ill health and first aid made known to all employees?	☐	☐	

Assessment of Standard 3:　　Met ☐　　Part met ☐　　Not met ☐

4	Supervision, training, information and instruction	Yes	No	Evidence/comments
A	Are employees provided with adequate competent supervision?	☐	☐	
B	Is initial health and safety information, instruction and training given to all new employees on recruitment?	☐	☐	
C	Is ongoing health and safety information, instruction and training provided to all employees?	☐	☐	
D	Is health and safety information, instruction and training recorded?	☐	☐	
E	How is the effectiveness of health and safety information, instruction and training assessed, and is the assessment recorded?	☐	☐	

Assessment of Standard 4:　　Met ☐　　Part met ☐　　Not met ☐

General health and safety assessment (continued)

	5 Work equipment and machinery	Yes	No	Evidence/comments
A	Is correct machinery and equipment provided to the appropriate standards?	☐	☐	
B	Is equipment adequately maintained?	☐	☐	
C	Are guards and control measures in place as determined through risk assessment?	☐	☐	
D	Are safe electrical systems and equipment provided and maintained?	☐	☐	

Assessment of Standard 5:　　　　Met ☐　　Part met ☐　　Not met ☐

	6 Personal protective equipment and clothing	Yes	No	Evidence/comments
A	Is PPE/C provided to employees as determined through risk assessment?	☐	☐	
B	Is training and information on the safe use of PPE/C provided to all employees?	☐	☐	
C	Is the proper use of PPE/C enforced?	☐	☐	
D	Is PPE/C maintained and replaced?	☐	☐	

Assessment of Standard 6:　　　　Met ☐　　Part met ☐　　Not met ☐

General health and safety assessment (continued)

7	Fire and emergencies	Yes	No	Evidence/comments
A	Is there a means of raising the alarm and is fire detection in place?	☐	☐	
B	Are there appropriate means of fighting fire in place?	☐	☐	
C	Are effective means of escape in place, including unobstructed routes and exits?	☐	☐	
D	Is there a named person(s) for emergencies?	☐	☐	
E	Are firefighting equipment, preventive measures and emergency arrangements maintained, including through tests and practice drills?	☐	☐	
F	Is a fire log/record book kept?	☐	☐	

Assessment of Standard 7:   Met ☐   Part met ☐   Not met ☐

8	Safe and healthy working environment	Yes	No	Evidence/comments
A	Are premises (structure, fabric, fixtures and fittings) safe and healthy (suitable, maintained and kept clean)?	☐	☐	
B	Is the working environment (temperature, lighting, space, ventilation, noise) an appropriate safe and healthy one?	☐	☐	
C	Are welfare facilities (toilets, washing, drinking, eating, changing) provided as appropriate and maintained?	☐	☐	

Assessment of Standard 8:   Met ☐   Part met ☐   Not met ☐

General health and safety assessment (continued)

9	General health and safety management	Yes	No	Evidence/comments
A	Does the employer consult and communicate with employees and allow them to participate in health and safety?	☐	☐	
B	Does the employer provide medical/health screening as appropriate and any required medical/health surveillance?	☐	☐	
C	Does the employer have access to competent health and safety advice/assistance?	☐	☐	
D	Does the employer review health and safety annually?	☐	☐	
E	Does the employer display the necessary signs and notices?	☐	☐	
F	Has an OSR1/ F9 been completed and sent to the enforcing authority?	☐	☐	
G	Is employers' liability insurance current and other insurance in place, as appropriate to the business undertaking?	☐	☐	Insurer's name: Policy number: Expiry date: Insurer informed of learners? Yes ☐ No ☐ N/A ☐
H	Does the employer assess, review and update employees' capabilities?	☐	☐	
I	Does the employer manage employees' work when it is away from the employer's own premises or when employees are placed with another employer or site?	☐	☐	
	Assessment of Standard 9:			Met ☐ Part met ☐ Not met ☐

General health and safety assessment (continued)

Assessment outcome

Recommendation   Accept ☐   Accept with action plan ☐   Reject ☐

Certificate of assessment issued? Yes ☐   No ☐   Certificate of achievement issued? Yes ☐   No ☐

Risk category   High ☐   Medium ☐   Low ☐

The employer or their representative
(Please sign to agree that this is an accurate record of the assessment)

Signed: Print name:

Job title: Date:

Funded organisation

Assessment undertaken by:

Name: Job title:

Quality assured by:

Name: Job title: Date:

Assessment type:

Initial assessment   Reassessment

Other (please specify):   Date of next assessment:

Additional comments/notes:

Form 2: Health and safety action plan

Ref	Action required	By whom	Target date	Completed (signed off)

Action plan prepared by: Agreed by:

Signed: Date:

Action plan review dates:

Form 3: Assessing health and safety for the learner

Learner's name:

Occupational area:

Employer's name and learner's work location(s):

Management of learner's/young person's health and safety (Standard 10)	Yes	No	Evidence/comments
A Has the employer assessed the risks to the learner/young person, taking into account their age, inexperience, immaturity and lack of awareness of risks?	☐	☐	
B Have the assessments taken into account any other special needs or circumstances including any disability and/or medical/health condition?	☐	☐	
C Has the employer put in place control measures for the learner/young person as a result of the assessments, and have they informed the learner and their supervisor(s)?	☐	☐	
D Detail any necessary prohibitions and restrictions identified by the risk assessments that apply to the learner/young person.			
E Does the employer provide competent supervision for learners/young persons, and do they have a designated person to take overall responsibility for them?	☐	☐	Name of supervisor(s):
F Does the employer provide an induction and ongoing information, instruction and training to learners/young persons reflecting the findings of the risk assessment, working environment, work activities, age, experience and any special needs?	☐	☐	
G Does the employer provide, free of charge, any necessary personal protective equipment and clothing (as determined by the risk assessment) and ensure its proper and effective use?	☐	☐	

Assessment of Standard 10: Met ☐ Part met ☐ Not met ☐

Assessing health and safety for the learner (continued)

Action plan

Ref	Action required	By whom	Target date	Completed (signed off)

Action plan prepared by: Agreed by:

Signed: Date:

Action plan review dates:

Confirming arrangements after assessment

After the assessment it is good practice to write to the employer, not only to confirm actions and development plans as part of your record-keeping system, but also to thank the employer and others who helped during the assessment process. It is very important to maintain good relationships with employers.

The post-assessment letter or email

Here is a suggested format for a follow-up letter.

Dear (insert name),

Health and Safety Assessment

Thank you for seeing me on (date to insert) and also (insert name) who helped me carry out the assessment.

As a result I can confirm that (the learners name) can be funded for (describe programme). I would like to confirm the matters we agreed during my visit and the action plan we put together:

If you have any queries please do not hesitate to contact me at the above address. I will next be visiting you to see (name of learner) on (date and time).

I would be grateful if you could let me know (by telephone or email) what you thought about the quality of the health and safety assessment and if there is anything that might be improved.

Yours sincerely,

Jim Smith
Assessor

5 Getting qualified

Everyone who carries out an assessment must be competent to do so. Not only must you demonstrate a commitment to learner health and safety but you must also meet legal and contractual requirements.

This section shows you how to become competent and certificated. It also tells you about the training and support available to assessors and organisations that employ assessors.

How to become competent

There are a number of ways to prove you are competent. One is to be assessed and certificated as competent against the national standard, *Health and Safety for People at Work* ENTO Unit D (see the box opposite), 'Review health and safety procedures in workplaces'. You can do this separately or where Unit D forms part of another qualification.

When choosing an assessor, you should make sure that they fulfil not only the Unit D standards but also those of the LSC in its statement on the competence of assessors (see page 60).

If you wish to be formally assessed for the competence award described in Unit D and fulfil the LSC's statement on competence, contact ENTO or a local centre accredited for the award.

As well as requiring competence to the national standard of Unit D, the LSC requires assessors to understand its health and safety procurement standards, reproduced in Appendix 2.

Unit D at a glance

Review health and safety procedures in workplaces

D1 Prepare to undertake a review of health and safety in a workplace

Performance criteria

You must ensure that:

1 you plan a work schedule for a review of health and safety conditions in accordance with agreed procedures;

2 your selected methods for the review are suitable for the workplace due to be reviewed;

3 you obtain authorisation for the review to take place from the person responsible for the workplace;

4 you prioritise your activities in the schedule of work to meet the timescale;

5 you obtain the necessary resources in time for the review to take place;

6 you brief other persons involved in the review to ensure they understand its purpose and the process to be undertaken;

7 you agree the documents and information to be used before conducting a review.

You must know and understand:

a the work areas and people who you are planning to review;

b what notice needs to be given before a review takes place;

c resources required for a review to take place;

d effective communication techniques.

D2 Carry out a review of workplace health and safety implementation

Performance criteria

You must ensure that:

1 your personal presentation when carrying out the review is sensitive to the workplace at all times;

2 your review covers working practices in the workplace including areas likely to need special checking;

3 you record, accurately, any difference between the content of previous records and the current situation;

4 you identify health and safety hazards that could result in serious harm to persons in the workplace, from:

   • working practices;

   • the work area.

5 in consultation with the responsible person, you list in priority order any non-compliance with health and safety regulations and laid down procedures;

6 you put forward sensible recommendations to control the hazards and agree an action plan for improving health and safety;

7 you record, fully, in accordance with established procedures;

   • the outcomes of the review of health and safety;

   • the action plan.

8 you agree with the responsible person a follow-up plan for monitoring and implementation of recommendations and corrective action.

You must know and understand:

a the industry/occupational area in which you are carrying out the review;

b effective interviewing techniques;

c presentational and communication skills;

d recording and reporting procedures;

e how to develop post-review follow-up plans and monitoring measures.

The LSC statement on competence

The national standard is set out in ENTO Unit D 'Review health and safety procedures in workplaces' summarised on page 59. The LSC have also issued the following statement about their expectations for the competence of assessors:

When learning takes place in an environment outside the control of the organisation the LSC funds, the LSC requires under the funding agreement/contract that the organisation makes an informed judgement about health and safety suitability prior to learning taking place in that environment.

One of the most common questions raised by those we fund is in respect to the competency required of those individuals who make that informed judgement on behalf of the organisation.

The LSC would want (see 'Extending Trust' report from the Bureaucracy Task Force) employers and their locations assessed only once every 1, 2 or 3 years depending on the risk (Note: Standard 10 relating to the individual will need to be agreed and met for each learner). This has the potential to save over £60m per year, but to do so there needs to be a core common standard of assessment (see the LSC's health and safety procurement standard). In addition, to rely upon another organisation's assessment there also needs to be a common satisfactory level of competence for those persons making the judgement over suitability.

The funding agreement asks for such persons to be sufficiently competent both in the occupational area and in health and safety. Without such it is difficult to see how an informed judgement can be reached over suitability and therefore how organisations can fulfil their duty of care and section 3 (Health and Safety at Work etc. Act) duties. However, it seems reasonable that the LSC explains its expectation over 'sufficiently'. In doing so we have consulted HSE on this matter. HSE endorse the standard of competence for assessors in ENTO Unit D ('Review health and safety procedures in workplaces') and this forms the basis of competence.

To be 'sufficient' an assessor needs to:

- understand[3] and be able to identify the main risks and control measures for the environment and occupational area being assessed (Unit D Element 2 under specific knowledge states 'you must know and understand the industry/occupational area in which you are carrying out the review');
- understand[4] the health and safety legislative requirements[5] applying to the employer and the learning/working environment and industry;
- fully understand the LSC's health and safety procurement standard;
- fully understand his/her employer's policy and procedures for assessing the suitability of placements;
- be aware of the needs of the particular learner and any particular health and safety requirements arising as a result (also see standard 10);
- be aware of his/her limitations and know when and where to seek advice or information; and
- have other competencies as detailed in ENTO Unit D not covered above (interview techniques, presentational and communication skills, developing post-review follow-up plans, etc.).

It is for the organisation the LSC funds to make the judgement of whether employees or contractors are sufficiently competent to assess on their behalf. In doing so organisations should seek competent advice.

Many LSC-funded organisations have asked about NEBOSH and IOSH qualifications. While these may provide some or all of the underpinning health and safety knowledge depending on the course it will not make a person competent. The LSC will therefore not be recommending a particular training course for assessors.

The LSC in working in partnership does wish to be as helpful as possible in this area. For example the LSC will recognise persons who achieve a competency-based qualification that includes Unit D or Unit D on its own. One example would be OCR 1417 (ENTO Units D and G (risk assessment)). In addition, those that are accredited to offer the Occupational Health and Safety Practice NVQ, level III should also be able to offer assessment against unit D, although this is not a mandatory unit in the NVQ.

Finally, the LSC does not require a person to have a qualification, only to be competent to do what is a very important job. The above information is provided as a benchmark to assist organisations to decide who should assess, or to identify development and training needs.

---

[3] 'Understand' does not mean that the assessor needs to be an expert or understand everything, but they must at least have a reasonable level of understanding given all the circumstances.

[4] as above

[5] This includes understanding the detailed requirements relating to young persons when the learner is a young person.

Checking your own competence

In preparing evidence and a portfolio to demonstrate your competence, you can do a number of things. One is to ask the following questions in relation to undertaking real assessments.

Competence self-check against Unit D1

The following questions are based on the requirements of Unit D1, *Prepare to undertake a review of health and safety procedures in a workplace*. You should aim to answer yes in each case. Use the space below to note the evidence for your answers.

	Yes	No
1 Have I planned a work schedule for a review of health and safety in accordance with agreed procedures?	☐	☐
2 What are to be my selected methods for the review, and are these suitable for the workplace to be reviewed?	☐	☐
3 Have I obtained authorisation for the review from the person responsible for the workplace?	☐	☐
4 Have I prioritised my work activities to meet the timescale?	☐	☐
5 Have I obtained the necessary resources in time for the review?	☐	☐
6 Have I ensured that other people involved understand its purpose and the process to be undertaken?	☐	☐
7 Have I agreed the documents and information to be used before conducting the review?	☐	☐

Summary of evidence for the above

Competence self-check against Unit D2

The following questions are based on the requirements of Unit D2, *Carry out a review of workplace health and safety implementation*. You should aim to answer yes in each case. Use the space below to note the evidence for your answers.

	Yes	No
1 Is my personal presentation when carrying out the review sensitive to the workplace at all times?	☐	☐
2 Does my review cover working practices in the workplace, including areas likely to need special checking?	☐	☐
3 Have I accurately recorded differences between the content of previous records and the current situation?	☐	☐
4 Have I identified health and safety hazards that could result in harm to people in the workplace from both working practices and the work area?	☐	☐
5 Have I – in consultation with the responsible person – listed in priority order any non-compliances with health and safety regulations or standards?	☐	☐
6 Have I put forward sensible recommendations to control the hazards and agreed an action plan for improving health and safety?	☐	☐
7 Have I recorded, in line with my procedures, the outcomes of the assessment and the action plan?	☐	☐
8 Have I agreed with the responsible person a follow-up plan for monitoring the implementation of recommendations and actions?	☐	☐

Summary of evidence for the above

Pre-assessment self-check

Here is a checklist you might like to use before doing an assessment.

Do I know and understand:	**Yes**	**No**
1 employers' and employees' legal duties for health and safety in the workplace as required by the Health and Safety at Work etc. Act 1974?	☐	☐
2 my responsibilities for health and safety as defined by specific legislation?	☐	☐
3 the policy and procedures for assessment?	☐	☐
4 when it is appropriate to wear personal protective equipment and clothing?	☐	☐
5 the particular health and safety risks which may be present in people's job roles?	☐	☐
6 the importance of being aware of hazards and risks which may arise in the type of workplace to be assessed?	☐	☐
7 when to report inappropriate procedures for assessing the workplace?	☐	☐

Job description for assessors

The job description for assessors must reflect their function and competence. The form below will not only help you identify who is competent but will also make clear what the job is about.

Workplace health and safety assessors

Identify any criteria you want to include in the assessor's job specification. Remember to pay particular attention to occupational competence and any special qualities you feel your assessors need. Make notes under the following headings:

Our assessors need to know:

Our assessors need to demonstrate:

Our assessors need the following:

Essential qualities:

Desirable qualities:

Remember...

Someone expert in health and safety might not make the best assessor. Equally, someone with the right occupational competence might not make the best assessor. This is why it is important to specify the qualities and skills you want from your assessors, to help not only recruit the right ones but for reasons of continuous professional development.

Further information

This section comprises:

- *a glossary of the terms used in this guide;*

- *information about ENTO and the Learning Network;*

- *lists of useful websites and publications.*

Glossary

BSI, the British Standards Institute, is the body responsible for developing nationally recognised standards to make life safer and more efficient.

Department for Education and Skills (DfES) represents the Government and sets policy for education and skills.

ENTO is the organisation responsible for national occupational standards for health and safety.

Funded organisation is a generic term used for organisations funded by the LSC. They include colleges, schools, training providers, LEA's, 6th forms and 6th-form colleges, education business partnerships, education business link organisations; and voluntary organisations.

HASPS – the LSC's Health and Safety Procurement Standards – are given in Appendix 2.

ILO, the International Labour Organisation, is a UN agency promoting social justice through the setting of minimum standards of basic human and labour rights.

Learner is a generic term used to describe people funded for learning, including pupils, students, trainees and apprentices.

Learning and Skills Council (LSC) is the funding body for learning in England and is responsible for taking forward Government and DfES policies in this area.

OHSAS – Occupational Health and Safety Assessment Series

Placement is the employer/location where the learner is being placed.

About ENTO

ENTO is an independent, self-financing organisation. Since 1988 its purpose has been to develop national vocational standards and qualifications (NVQs) and to provide products and services to support these standards and qualifications.

Our work helps people develop their level of competence and skills, and aims to meet the needs of employees and employers as well as learners. We are also responsible for promoting and monitoring the **matrix** Standard, a quality standard for any organisation that gives information, advice and guidance.

ENTO represents, across all sectors, people whose occupation requires them to deal with people in the workplace. This includes people in the field of information, advice and guidance; learning and development trainers; HR people; recruitment consultants; trade union representatives involved in learning; and health and safety at work practitioners.

Because of this role, the people for whom ENTO standards and qualifications have been developed have a significant influence on the take-up of vocational qualifications throughout the workplace and at all levels. ENTO maintains 9 suites of National Occupational Standards covering 11 occupational areas, 23 NVQs, 4 Apprenticeships and 3 suites of non-qualification-based standards.

The Learning Network

The Learning Network is an online support network run by ENTO for anyone who delivers, assesses or verifies NVQs and SVQs. The network's main aim is to enhance continuous professional development by offering up-to-date information, a forum for discussion and sharing of best practice, and providing the opportunity to influence what is happening in the arena of assessment and verification.

To find out more about the benefits of membership, email: info@ento.co.uk

Alternatively, visit www.thelearningnetworkonline.com or call 02920 462572.

Useful websites and publications

Websites

www.safelearner.info

www.dfes.gov.uk

www.lsc.gov.uk

www.hse.gov.uk

www.nebosh.org.uk

www.aoc.co.uk

www.learningproviders.org.uk

www.thenetrisk.com

www.tuc.org.uk

www.teachernet.gov.uk

www.young-worker.co.uk

HSE publications

(See also www.hsebooks.co.uk and HSE infoline 08701 545 500.)

- HSG165 *Young people at work: a guide for employers*
- HSG65 *Successful health and safety management*
- HSG199 *Managing health and safety on work experience*
- L21 *Management of health and safety: Approved Code of Practice*
- *Essentials of Health and Safety at Work* (HSE) ISBN 0 7176 0716X

A variety of HSE leaflets is available to download from HSE's website, including:

- INDG163(rev) *Five steps to risk assessment*
- INDG213 *Health and Safety Training*
- *Health and safety law: what you should know*
- INDG259 *An introduction to health and safety*

LSC publications

1. *Supervising the safe learner: Guidance for Providers* (MISC/0613/03)

2. *Supervising the safe learner: Guidance for Employers* (MISC/0611/03)

3. *Guidance for supervising learners* (MISC/0610/03)

4. *Pocket Guide to Supervising Learner Health and Safety* (MISC/0612/03)

5. *Standards for Health and Safety: Information for employers on the LSC's health and safety standards for learners* (LSC/AA000/1127/04)

All the above are available from the publication enquires line, 0870 900 6800.

For further guidance, good practice and links visit www.safelearner.info

Other publications

DfES, *Supervising learners' health and safety* (GPS/RS/7).

Appendices

This section contains:

- *a summary of the LSC's contractual clauses on learner health, safety and welfare;*

- *the LSC's health and safety procurement standards (HASPS);*

- *an audit tool for managers and competent persons.*

Appendix 1
Summary of LSC contractual requirements

Learner health, safety and welfare

- The LSC requires the co-operation of contractors and the provision of information that assures that standards for learner health and safety are met.

- The LSC requires contractors to ensure that learning takes place in safe, healthy and supportive environments that meet the needs of learners.

- Those funded must:
  - operate an effective health and safety management system such as in HSE's *Successful Health and Safety Management* (HSG65);
  - continually seek to raise standards and carry out learner health and safety self-assessment;
  - promote good practice and the LSC's safe learner concept;
  - make an informed judgement of health and safety suitability when learning takes place with another employer/location. To be suitable the employer/location must at least meet the LSC's health and safety procurement standard;
  - periodically review health and safety standards of employer/locations and learners;
  - have access to competent advice/persons;
  - use only persons competent to assess the suitability of learning locations/employers used for learning;
  - maintain records in relation to learner health and safety including assessments of suitability, monitoring, assessments of learner health and safety understanding; agreements and information in relation to accidents and incidents to learners;
  - take into account HSE-approved codes of practice guidance from the HSE and LSC;
  - ensure that learners receive effective information, instruction, training and supervision based on an assessment of risk;
  - ensure that risks to learners who are young persons or have special needs are reduced to the lowest level that is reasonably practicable;
  - ensure that learner health and safety understanding is periodically assessed;
  - ensure effective co-operation and co-ordination with others so that respective responsibilities are clear in respect to learner health and safety;
  - ensure that young persons and vulnerable learners are protected through proper recruitment and other methods. This may include formal checks for child protection purposes if appropriate;
  - ensure that where learning is managed by others or sub-contracted that adequate agreements are put in place including the matters above.

Appendix 2
The LSC's health and safety procurement standards (HASPS)

Safe, healthy and supportive environment

1   The employer has a health and safety policy

   A There is a clear commitment to health and safety (a written policy statement where there are five or more employees).

   B Responsibilities for health and safety are clearly stated (recorded where there are five or more employees).

   C Arrangements for health and safety are clearly stated including the control measures identified from risk assessment (recorded where there are five or more employees).

   D The commitment, responsibilities and arrangements for health and safety are communicated to all employees.

2   The employer has assessed risks and put in place control measures to prevent or reduce risks

   A Risk assessments have been carried out and significant risks identified.

   B Significant risks have been recorded (optional where less than five employees).

   C Control measures have been identified and implemented as a result of risk assessment.

   D Employees (and others as appropriate) are explained the significant risks and control measures.

3   The employer has made adequate arrangements for dealing with accidents and incidents including the provision of first aid

   A Adequate arrangements for first-aid materials have been made.

   B Adequate arrangements for first-aid persons have been made.

   C All accidents and first-aid treatment rendered are recorded.

   D All legally reportable accidents, incidents and ill-health are/will be reported to the enforcing authority and investigated.

   E Accident, incident, ill-health and first-aid arrangements are made known to all employees and others as appropriate.

4   The employer provides employees with effective supervision, training, information and instruction

   A Employees are provided with adequate competent supervision.

   B Initial health and safety information, training and instruction are given to all new employees on recruitment.

C Ongoing health and safety information, training and instruction are provided to all employees and others as appropriate.

D Information, instruction and training are recorded.

E Effectiveness of training etc. is assessed and assessments recorded.

5 The employer provides and maintains suitable and appropriate equipment and machinery, which is safe and without risks to health

A The employer provides the correct equipment to the appropriate standard.

B Equipment is adequately maintained.

C Guards and control measures are in place as determined from risk assessment.

D Safe electrical systems and equipment are provided and maintained.

6 The employer has made arrangements for the provision and use of necessary personal protective equipment and clothing (PPE/C)

A PPE/C is provided for employees as determined from risk assessment.

B Training and information on PPE/C use has been provided to employees.

C The proper use of PPE/C is enforced.

D PPE/C is maintained and replaced.

7 The employer has made arrangements for fire and other foreseeable emergencies

A A means of raising the alarm and fire/emergency detection is in place.

B Appropriate means of fire fighting are in place.

C Effective means of escape are in place including escape routes and unobstructed exits.

D There is a named person(s) for emergencies.

E Arrangements are maintained, including tests and drills.

F A fire log is kept.

8 The employer provides a safe and healthy working environment

A Premises (structure, fabric, fixtures and fittings) are safe and healthy (suitable, maintained and kept clean).

B The working environment (temperature, lighting, space, ventilation, noise) is appropriate, safe and healthy.

C Welfare facilities (toilets, washing, drinking, eating, changing) are provided as appropriate and maintained.

9   The employer manages health and safety

A   The employer consults and communicates with employees on health and safety and allows them to participate in health and safety.

B   The employer provides medical/health screening as appropriate and any required medical surveillance.

C   The employer has access to competent advice.

D   The employer reviews health and safety annually.

E   The employer provides and displays necessary signs and notices.

F   Notification has been given to the enforcing authority as appropriate

G   Employers' liability insurance[6] is current and other insurance is in place as appropriate to the business undertaking.

H   The employer assesses, reviews and updates employee's capabilities.

I   The employer manages employee work when it is away from the employer's own premises or when placed with another employer/site.

10   The employer manages learners'/young persons' health, safety and welfare

A   The employer has assessed the risks to any learner/young person taking account of his/her age (inexperience, immaturity, etc.) and any other special needs or circumstances including any disability and/or medical/health condition.

B   The employer has put in place control measures for learners/young persons as a result of 10A. and informed the learner and his/her supervisor.

C   The employer has identified any necessary prohibitions and restrictions that apply to any learner/young person as part of 10A and 10B.

D   The employer provides competent supervision[7] for any learner/young person and has a designated person to take overall responsibility for any learner/young person.

E   The employer provides an induction and ongoing information, instruction and training to any learner/young person reflecting the result of the risk assessment, environment, tasks and the learner's/young person's age, experience and any special needs.

F   The employer provides free of charge any necessary (determined from the risk assessment) personal protective equipment and clothing to the learner and ensures its proper and effective use.

---

[6]   This includes informing insurers and/or brokers where appropriate of the learner(s)' presence/programme.

[7]   In some cases where the learner is a child, this may require formal checks of suitability for reasons of child protection.

Appendix 3
An audit tool for managers and competent persons

This audit tool for managers of assessors and for competent persons uses a list of questions based on this guide and on good practice. You may need to expand the questions and to use several sheets of paper to record your answers, and the sources of evidence for your answers.

Use the audit as a tool to identify weaknesses (as well as strengths), so that you can produce an action plan and recommendations to improve what you are doing already.

Question	Yes	Not sure	No
Do we have a written policy for health and safety assessment (or for placing learners with other employers in other workplaces)? (How effective is the policy? Do people know about it?)	☐	☐	☐
Do we have clear written procedures for health and safety assessment?	☐	☐	☐
Do we train our assessors?	☐	☐	☐
Have we assessed the risk of placing learners with others?	☐	☐	☐
Have we put in place control measures to reduce the risk to learners and to assessors?	☐	☐	☐
Have we produced a flowchart of the procedures and documented them?	☐	☐	☐
Have we set standards for assessment and what constitutes a 'safe, healthy and supportive environment'?	☐	☐	☐
Do we record health and safety assessments?	☐	☐	☐
Do we provide employers with a copy of our assessment?	☐	☐	☐
Do we offer or provide certificates of assessment to employers?	☐	☐	☐
Do we offer or provide certificates of achievement to employers?	☐	☐	☐
Have we set minimum standards for the competence of assessors?	☐	☐	☐

What evidence do we have?	Development/action

Question	Yes	Not sure	No
Do we analyse the training needs of assessors?	☐	☐	☐
Do we support assessors?	☐	☐	☐
Do we record heath and safety assessments?	☐	☐	☐
Do we assess and agree individual learner requirements?	☐	☐	☐
Do we have a formal written agreement with employers setting out the health and safety requirements and responsibilities?	☐	☐	☐
Do we support supervisors?	☐	☐	☐
Do we agree action or development plans with employers where standards are not met or partly met?	☐	☐	☐
Do we quality assure assessments?	☐	☐	☐
Do we sample or quality assure assessments with employers?	☐	☐	☐
Do we set some performance indicators or measures of success for assessments and assessors?	☐	☐	☐
Do we communicate and share necessary information with the employer, supervisor, learner, other funded organisations and the LSC?	☐	☐	☐
Do we have an agreement or contract that includes the appropriate health and safety clauses?	☐	☐	☐
Do we have a pre-assessment procedure?	☐	☐	☐
Do we inform and communicate our policy and procedures on assessment?	☐	☐	☐
Have we consulted with the local office of the LSC and their health and safety person on our procedures?	☐	☐	☐

What evidence do we have?	Development/action